Practice in the Basic Skills

English 4

D0256195

Contents

Published by Collins Educational
An imprint of HarperCollins*Publishers* Ltd
77-85 Fulham Palace Road
London W6 8JB

www.**Collins**Education.com
On-line support for schools and colleges

© Derek Newton and David Smith 2003
First published 1978
This edition published 2003
Reprinted 10 9

ISBN-13 978-0-00-717715-8
ISBN-10 0-00-717715-1

The authors assert the moral right to be identified
as the authors of this work.

British Library Cataloguing in Publication Data
A catalogue record for this book is available from
the British Library.

Illustrated by A Rodger

Printed by Martins the Printers Ltd,
Berwick upon Tweed

Nouns

A Write out the **nouns** in each of these sentences.

 1 The dog ran away over the field.
 2 The bananas and custard were in a dish.
 3 Elephants are used to carry logs.
 4 Wine is made from grapes.
 5 The policeman stopped all cars and lorries.
 6 The children and teachers enjoyed the circus.
 7 The lifeguard swam to the struggling swimmer.
 8 Last night Tom read a book and went for a walk.
 9 Porridge, bacon, egg and toast make a good breakfast.
10 The helicopter landed safely on a football field behind a school.

B Here are the meanings of ten **nouns**. They all begin with the letter **c**.

 e.g. a long, green vegetable used in salads   **cucumber**

 1 A bird that lays its eggs in other birds' nests.
 2 The roof of a room.
 3 Cement, sand, stones and water mixed together.
 4 A drink made from apple juice.
 5 A person who buys from a shop.
 6 A child of your uncle or aunt.
 7 A machine for lifting heavy objects.
 8 A food made from sour milk.
 9 A list of the days, weeks and months of the year.
10 The grub from which a moth or butterfly comes.

Adjectives (1)

A Write out the **adjectives** in these sentences.

1 The weather was damp and foggy.
2 The blind dog was found near the wooden bridge.
3 Peter is short and fat, but Sam is tall and slim.
4 Tigers are large, powerful, striped cats found in Asia.
5 The small yacht battled against strong winds and a rough sea.
6 Magpies have slender, long tails and short wings.
7 The fast, thrilling race excited the large crowd.
8 The fisherman wore a thick, blue sweater and a red, woollen hat.
9 Dodos are extinct, flightless birds which looked like giant pigeons.
10 The brave explorers were exhausted after their dangerous journey through
   the hot, humid jungle.

B Choose the correct **adjective** from the list to complete each sentence.

empty	victorious	fatal	nourishing	huge
courageous	priceless	fragrant	difficult	fierce

1 A _____ painting was stolen from the art gallery.
2 A _____ accident occurred on the mountain.
3 The _____ dog bit the postman.
4 _____ roses are very pleasant in a garden.
5 Their voices echoed in the _____ room.
6 The _____ whale opened its mouth and swallowed the boat.
7 The _____ fireman rescued the old lady from the blazing house.
8 The _____ team was given a great welcome by the town.
9 The general had to make a _____ decision.
10 After five days adrift on a raft the sailor enjoyed a _____ meal.

C Now use each of these **adjectives** in sentences of your own.

Verbs (1)

A Write out the **verbs** in these sentences.

1 The old lady slipped then fell on the icy road.
2 When Heather finished her book she returned it to the library.
3 Paul ate his breakfast quickly then ran to school.
4 It took Mark two hours to make his model aeroplane.
5 After the keeper fed the lions she cleaned the monkey's cage.
6 In the morning mum baked cakes, cleaned the windows and washed some clothes.
7 I saw the helicopter rescue two bathers from the sea.
8 The racing car sped along the straight, but braked too hard on the bend and skidded into bales of straw.
9 The astronauts climbed into their capsule and checked their controls.
10 Poor Sandra fell off her bike and broke her arm.

B Choose the correct **verb** from the list to complete each sentence.

perched	repeated	flickered	collided	marooned
measured	collapsed	interrupted	swooped	shattered

1 Mandy carefully _____ the length of the corridor.
2 The two ships _____ in the fog.
3 The kestrel _____ on its prey.
4 I saw the parrot _____ on the top branch of the tree.
5 When Wendy finished the race she _____ on the track.
6 The candle _____ in the draughty cellar.
7 The ball hit the window and _____ the glass.
8 The teacher _____ the question but still Simon didn't know the answer.
9 The rude boy _____ his dad when he was on the telephone.
10 Robinson Crusoe was _____ on a desert island.

C Now use each of these **verbs** in sentences of your own.

Adverbs (1)

A Write out the **adverbs** in these sentences.

1 The cat climbed swiftly up the tree.
2 The dog barked loudly at the boys.
3 The sun shone brightly for the carnival.
4 Grandad was sitting comfortably in his chair.
5 Our school sports day takes place annually.
6 The tired old lady walked wearily up the hill.
7 The farmer walked slowly across the field but when he saw the injured cow he ran quickly towards it.
8 The teacher remembered clearly that Alec's homework was not given in on time.
9 The leopard sprang suddenly from the tree but the antelope cleverly avoided it.
10 John came immediately but Mark arrived late.

B Choose the correct **adverb** from the list to complete each sentence.

soundly	anxiously	fiercely	correctly	tunefully
foolishly	bitterly	silently	frantically	briefly

1 Helen answered the question _____ .
2 When Tom was on holiday he spent his money _____ .
3 After their long walk on the hills the children slept _____ .
4 Peter was trapped in the mud and he shouted _____ .
5 The guard dog growled _____ when he heard a noise.
6 Carolyn had to explain _____ because she was in a hurry.
7 The burglar crept _____ up the stairs.
8 Crowds of people waited _____ for news of the overdue aircraft.
9 Our choir sang _____ in the concert.
10 Jane wept _____ when her bicycle was stolen.

C Now use each **adverb** in sentences of your own.

Alphabetical order

A Write the names of these objects in alphabetical order.

B Write the following lines of words in alphabetical order.

1 cage   runway   warrior   hobby   meat   beach
2 nylon   smell   acorn   grass   white   quiz
3 vein   puzzle   cry   jelly   duck   frost

C Write the names of these objects in alphabetical order.

D Write the following lines of words in alphabetical order.

1 potato   pea   public   pier   prize   path
2 bite   boat   bread   bed   black   bulb
3 witch   wrist   worm   whip   wasp   weak

E Write the names of these objects in alphabetical order.

F Write the following lines of words in alphabetical order.

1 spun   speak   spy   spin   spoon   spade
2 prison   prime   prize   price   pride   princess
3 channel   chalk   chatter   chameleon   chain   chart

Sentences

A Write the following so that the **beginnings** are matched with the correct **endings**.

beginning	ending
1 The man is putting his hat	so Jean put up her umbrella.
2 Dad is wearing a watch	at the signal.
3 Sam is painting	to rescue the sailors.
4 It was raining heavily	on his wrist.
5 The train is stopping	at Manchester Airport.
6 Nicky is cutting bread	on his head.
7 The Jumbo jet is landing	with a knife.
8 The lifeboat is speeding	the back door.

B Use your own words to **end** the following:

1 Paul tried very hard _____ .
2 There was great excitement at the zoo _____ .
3 Lisa was very sad when _____ .
4 Just as Simon opened the door _____ .
5 Everyone dashed for cover when _____ .

C Use your own words at the **beginning** to make complete sentences.

1 _____ so we ran off as fast as we could.
2 _____ because the roads were so icy.
3 _____ and we built a huge bonfire.
4 _____ with all his strength.
5 _____ but the keys were found.

Compound words

A Write the name of each picture. Show the two words which form the
compound word.

e.g. **neck** + **lace**   **necklace**

1

2

3

4

5

6

7

8

9

10

11

12

B Write down another **compound word** beginning with the first part of
the word you have written for each picture.

e.g. **1 head**land or **head**line

Vocabulary and spelling (1)

A The first letters of the answers spell out a **country**.

frozen water   _ _ _ _

a place where light meals are served   _ _ f _

the largest living land animal   _ _ e _ _ _ _ _

a place where books are kept   _ _ _ r _ _ _ _

all the letters from A to Z   _ _ _ _ a _ _ _ _

a frightening dream   _ _ g _ _ _ _ _ _

a yellow wild flower   _ _ n _ _ _ _ _ _

B The first letters of the answers spell out a **mammal**.

a powerful machine for levelling ground   _ u _ _ _ _ _ _ _

very old   _ _ _ i _ _ _ _

to get out of the way   _ o _ _ _ _

a slow-moving river of ice   _ _ _ _ c _ _ _ _

a bird of prey   _ _ _ _ l _

a large cattle farm   _ _ _ _ _ h

C The first letters of the answers spell out a **fruit**.

the eighth month of the year   _ _ _ u _ _ _

meat from a pig   _ _ r _

wealthy   _ _ _ h

a very young child   _ _ f _ _ _ _

a person who buys from a shop   _ _ _ t _ _ _ _ _

a sea animal with eight legs   _ _ _ o _ _ _ _

the shape made by joining three
    straight sides   _ _ _ a _ _ _ _ _

Singular and plural

The names of the things illustrated below are nouns that form their **plurals** in different ways. Write down each noun, together with its **plural** form.

e.g. **wolf—wolves**

1	**2**	**3**
4	**5**	**6**
7	**8**	**9**
10	**11**	**12**
13	**14**	**15**

Mixed bag (1)

Your dictionary will help you to answer these.

A Write the **opposites** to these words.

1 thick   _____
2 open   _____
3 sweet   _____
4 single   _____
5 ugly   _____

6 courteous   _____
7 real   _____
8 temporary   _____
9 success   _____
10 public   _____

B Write the words that have **similar meanings** to these.

1 rapid   _____
2 sorrow   _____
3 opportunity _____
4 cunning   _____
5 compel   _____

6 massive   _____
7 sacred   _____
8 abundant   _____
9 extravagant _____
10 origin   _____

C All these jumbled letters will make names of **sports**.
Write down the correct words. The first letter of each is given.

1 LAFBOOTL   F_____
2 BRYGU   R_____
3 TENLABL   N_____
4 TCRCKEI   C_____
5 QUSSHA   S_____

6 MMSWNIGI   S_____
7 OHECYK   H_____
8 STINNE   T_____
9 GANGNIL   A_____
10 DMNINOABT B_____

Gender

A Write the **masculine** forms of these nouns.

1 grandmother	**4** manageress	**7** sow
2 stewardess	**5** mare	**8** duchess
3 peahen	**6** headmistress	**9** nun

B Write the **feminine** forms of these nouns.

1 actor	**4** bachelor	**7** widower
2 stag	**5** male	**8** father-in-law
3 gentleman	**6** colt	**9** tom-cat

C In each pair illustrated below there is one **masculine** and one **feminine**. Write out the correct names of each.

Picture story

Look carefully at the pictures then write a story that tells all that happened.
Think of a title.

These words will help you.

youth river bridge watching snapped fall panic swimming
desperate drowning weir unconscious revive ambulance mayor
award bravery proud

Verbs (2)
Past tense

A Complete these sentences by using the **past tense** of the verb in brackets.

1 Tom felt proud when he _____ hands with the team captain. (shake)
2 Mary _____ on to the bank of the river until help came. (hold)
3 The cat _____ on to the bird table. (spring)
4 The town hall clock _____ seven and Jayne hadn't arrived. (strike)
5 Sonia _____ a letter of thanks to the librarian. (write)
6 The cars and buses _____ at the traffic lights. (stop)
7 I _____ swimming _____ the best of all sports. (think, is)
8 We _____ down to Tenby and _____ all the hotels _____ full. (drive, find, are)
9 I _____ to a football match and afterwards I _____ a meal. (go, have)
10 Mark's nose _____ a lot when he _____ off his bicycle. (bleed, fall)

Past participle

B Use the **participle** of the verb in brackets to complete each sentence.

1 The old man was _____ to be a tramp. (know)
2 Martin had _____ for a long walk. (go)
3 Dick's ankle was _____ after the game. (swell)
4 The jewels were _____ under the floorboards. (hide)
5 Not many books have been _____ by children. (write)
6 After we had _____ our tea we went on the pond which was _____ over. (eat, freeze)
7 The nest had _____ to the ground but the young had _____ away. (fall, fly)
8 Our school was _____ by Leigh and Woodvale had _____ to Neston. (beat, lose)
9 Our kittens have _____ a lot since they were _____ on milk and fish. (grow, feed)
10 I have _____ the grass and Paul has _____ the edges of the lawn. (mow, trim)

Homonyms

A Here are illustrated eight pairs of common nouns. Each pair is often confused because they sound the same.

Write out what each pair is. The first one is done for you.

1 **a** beech **b** beach

B Now write sentences for each of the nouns.

Rhyming words

A Which words in brackets **rhyme** with the word in bold type?

1	**touch**	(pouch, much, rush, coach, such)
2	**gnaw**	(gnu, knee, gnarl, raw, gnat)
3	**use**	(us, loose, fuse, noose, puss)
4	**know**	(cow, now, low, sew, shoe)
5	**nought**	(route, rout, caught, laughed, sought)
6	**dreamt**	(gleamed, creamed, unkempt, steamed, cement)
7	**both**	(cloth, loathe, growth, botch, booth)
8	**soul**	(howl, bowl, foul, fowl, foal)
9	**clear**	(bear, near, dare, wear, deer)
10	**love**	(move, dove, wove, drove, above)

B Complete these sentences sensibly by choosing a word which **rhymes** with the word in bold type.

1	**cane**	There was a _____ on the carpet where the coffee was spilled.
2	**rude**	I am afraid Mr. Rigby is in a very bad _____.
3	**vain**	Pull on the _____ and the horse will slow down.
4	**fear**	There was a loud _____ when our team scored.
5	**rot**	Ted Bell's _____ won the 'Round Britain' race.
6	**haste**	Did you see the rabbit being _____ by the dog?
7	**sea**	I'm sorry but I do not _____ with you.
8	**glum**	The hungry birds ate every _____ of bread.
9	**know**	In autumn and spring the farmers _____ their seed.
10	**worse**	Vicky was sure she put her money in her _____.

Prepositions

Write a sentence about each picture and underline the **preposition**.
The list will help you.
The first one could be: The policeman dives into the river.

across	behind	amongst	through	off	up	into	above
between	under	after	over	against	on	by	

Direct speech (1)

A Copy out the words which are actually **spoken** in the following sentences.

1 "Where are my slippers?" asked Dad.
2 "Come to my house on Saturday morning," said Oliver.
3 The teacher looked at her watch and said, "You're late."
4 "Yes," answered the boy, counting his money carefully.
5 "Paul said he was very hungry," said Heather.
6 "Stop looking!" shouted Roger, "I've found it."
7 "Washington is the capital of the USA," replied Malcolm.
8 "Penalty!" roared the crowd, as their striker was tripped in the penalty area.
9 "Good morning," the milkman said. "You're up early."
10 "Try to write an interesting story, Jenny," said Mrs. Rigby.
11 "Today has been a happy day," shouted Ian. "Not for me though," replied Ann, "I've lost my purse."
12 "I was asleep," cried Alison. "The thunder woke me up. I'm frightened. Please come and talk to me."

B Write sentences containing **direct speech** "_____" about each of the following:

1 something you said to your teacher
2 something you asked the policeman
3 something you whispered to your friend
4 something you shouted to your dog
5 something your teacher told you to do
6 something you asked your dad or mum

Verbs (3)

A Complete these sentences by choosing suitable **verbs** to fit in the spaces.

1 Hillary and Tensing _____ Everest in 1953.
2 Captain Webb _____ the English Channel in 1875.
3 In 1954 Roger Bannister _____ the mile in under four minutes.
4 Neil Armstrong and Edwin Aldrin _____ on the moon in 1969.
5 The joiner _____ a hole through the piece of wood.
6 The thief _____ with a large sum of money.
7 The leaves of the tree _____ in the breeze.
8 The judge _____ sentence on the guilty man.
9 Mark _____ a hat-trick for the school team.
10 The lorry _____ on the greasy road and hit a wall.
11 The house was unsafe so it was _____ .
12 Smoking is _____ in all theatres and cinemas.

B Write the **verbs**.

1 u n __ __ __ __   to take the cover off a parcel
2 l __ __ __ __ __   to get to know something; to study
3 h __ __ __ __   to go quickly
4 d __ __ __ __ __ y   to ruin completely
5 s __ __ __ __   to slip along something smooth, such as ice
6 r __ __ __ __ __   to save someone or something from danger
7 s c __ __ __ __ __   to throw things around in all directions
8 g __ __ __ __   to look after; to keep safe
9 r __ __ __ __ __   to say or do again
10 w r __ __ __ __ __ __   to move by twisting and turning

Better words

A Rewrite these sentences using a better word than **got**.

1 The workman **got** down the ladder very quickly.
2 By using a file they **got** out of prison.
3 I **got** a nice present on my birthday.
4 "At last he's **got** what I'm trying to explain to him," said the teacher.
5 John has **got** many stamps since he started the hobby.
6 Sharon **got** her homework finished quite early.
7 Since school closed for summer, he's **got** very silly.
8 Michael has **got** the puppy upstairs.

B Rewrite these sentences using a better word than **nice**.

1 Skiing is such a **nice** experience.
2 My medicine has not a very **nice** taste.
3 We saw a **nice** film about diving for treasure.
4 Those strawberry cream tarts were **nice**.
5 It's a change to see you looking so **nice**.
6 Kim is a **nice** dog, and in no way is she silly.
7 I hope the weather is **nice** so that we can sit on the beach.
8 After finishing the cross country we had a **nice** drink of orange.

C Rewrite these sentences using a better word than **said**.

1 "Am I on the right road for Marlborough?" **said** the driver.
2 "Be careful! The roof is going to fall in," **said** the policeman.
3 Bill moved close to Tom and **said**, "Keep this a close secret."
4 "I think you would be better to make another one," **said** Mum.
5 The injured girl lay still on the playground. "My leg hurts," she **said**.
6 At assembly the headmistress **said** that we could all watch the sports.
7 "Give me one more chance," **said** the prisoner.
8 "You cannot park your car here," **said** the traffic warden.

Adverbs (2)

A Complete these sentences by adding suitable **adverbs**.

1 The lifeguard swam _____ as there was no time to lose.
2 The fireman struggled _____ but he could not reach the trapped man.
3 The thrush sang _____ as it perched on the garden fence.
4 The guard dog barked _____ as the two men went towards the gate.
5 Brian and Derek played _____ and woke up the baby.
6 The rain fell _____ so we all ran under the tree.
7 The aeroplane landed _____ in spite of the fog.
8 Everyone laughed _____ when they watched the clowns.
9 Pam worked her sums _____ and finished _____ .
10 I bumped into the old man _____ as he turned _____ into the street.
11 The storm arose _____ , and we rowed _____ for the shore.
12 The angry bull rushed _____ at the boys who had to climb _____ up the oak tree.

B Use the following pairs of words, **verbs** and **adverbs**, in sentences of your own.

1 limped slowly
2 crashed heavily
3 marched smartly
4 shone brightly
5 argued noisily
6 discovered accidentally
7 talked quietly
8 swam strongly
9 cried frantically
10 laughed merrily
11 listened patiently
12 increased rapidly

Collective nouns

A Write suitable **collective nouns** for the following.

1 an _____ of soldiers
2 a _____ of books
3 a _____ of insects
4 a _____ of teachers
5 a _____ of wolves

6 a _____ of stairs
7 a _____ of furniture
8 a _____ of stamps
9 an _____ of poems
10 a _____ of whales

B What would you expect people to be doing in the groups named below?

1 a choir
2 a crew
3 a party
4 a mob

5 an orchestra
6 a bench
7 a queue
8 a troupe

C There are six pictures below. Each can be described by a **plural** noun or by a **collective** noun. Name each picture in both ways. The first one is done for you.

1 puppies—litter
2
3
4
5
6

Mixed bag (2)

A Complete these sentences by using **past** or **passed**.

1 Alan _____ his driving test.
2 The boy ran _____ our door.
3 History is the study of the _____ .
4 The time _____ quickly at the football match.
5 The racing cars sped _____ the pits.
6 Gary _____ the ball through the hoop.
7 Heavy rain during the _____ week caused flooding.
8 For the _____ year John and Sue have been in Miss Green's class.
9 Fiona tiptoed _____ the sleeping dog.
10 Old people talk about the _____ rather than the present or future.

B Complete the sentences by choosing the correct word from the brackets.

1 Day is to sun as night is to (dark, stars, moon).
2 Fur is to rabbit as feathers are to (fox, animal, owl, cage).
3 Hat is to head as sock is to (shoe, foot, arm, hand).
4 Door is to wood as coat is to (hat, gloves, cloth, trousers).
5 Young is to old as early is to (baby, now, late, child).
6 Calf is to cow as puppy is to (cat, bull, playful, dog).

C Complete these sentences by choosing the correct word from the brackets.

1 Darren has (fell, fall, fallen) down the stairs.
2 Anybody (is, are) allowed to borrow a book.
3 He was (laying, lying, laid) on the town hall lawn.
4 They have (sang, sung, singed) that song at our concert.
5 Susan had (ate, eaten, eat) all her sweets.
6 The teacher has (spoke, speak, spoken) to Nicola about it.
7 Tom ran quickly to the station but he (mist, missed) the train.
8 Nobody has (never, ever) climbed that mountain.
9 The boy hasn't (nothing, anything) to do with it.
10 My dad is (learning, teaching) me to play chess.

Pronouns

A Write out the **pronouns** in the following sentences.

1 Paul's uncle took him to watch the FA cup final.
2 Heather reminded me that she should go swimming.
3 The scoutmaster told us that we must not swim in the river.
4 We always liked to listen to him telling jokes.
5 Mark told Dawn that he would take her to the cinema.
6 Would you like to speak to them now?
7 The pilot told them they would be landing soon.
8 You must be careful when you use his air rifle.
9 The dog hid his bone but forgot where it was hidden!
10 The teacher always allows us to take our books home.

B Write out these sentences and put a **pronoun** from the list in place of the words in bold type.

| they | us | he | it | him | she | them | her |

1 Wait for **David** in the park.
2 **Sally** gave **Joan** a birthday present.
3 Why doesn't **Mr. Aitken** give **Mr. Perkins** a chance?
4 **Mrs. Bladen and Mrs. Makin** cannot find **the letter**.
5 **Carol** is not going with **Tom, Heather and Susie**.
6 Pick **the flowers** and take some to **Mrs. Holmes**.
7 **Joan** cannot take **Brenda** because **John** has the car.
8 **Mr. Thomas** told **John** to put **the hamsters** back in the cage.
9 **Danny and Patrick** met **Jean**.
10 **John** met **David and me**.

Similes

A This list of words will help you to write out the **similes** connected with the following pictures of animals.

| agile | graceful | busy | wise | brave | cunning | slippery | slow |

1 as _____
as ___ _____

2 as _____
as ___ _____

3 as _____
as ___ _____

4 as _____
as ___ _____

5 as _____
as ___ _____

6 as _____
as ___ _____

7 as _____
as ___ _____

8 as _____
as ___ _____

B Complete these **similes** by choosing the best word in the brackets.

1 as blind as a (chicken, deer, rabbit, bat)
2 as flat as a (kettle, loaf, pancake, saucer)
3 as timid as a (lion, mouse, giant, mule)
4 as proud as a (rabbit, mouse, peacock, wolf)
5 as happy as a (lark, pig, daisy, serpent)
6 as thin as a (house, football, rake, king)

C Complete these **similes** by adding suitable words.

1 as tough as _____
2 as dry as _____
3 as good as _____
4 as keen as _____
5 as sweet as _____
6 as cold as _____

7 as _____ as a new pin
8 as _____ as two peas
9 as _____ as a cucumber
10 as _____ as coal
11 as _____ as toast
12 as _____ as clockwork

Direct speech (2)

A Write out these sentences putting in the speech marks ''_____''.

  1 I am going home, said Mark.
  2 Bring my books, please, said Mr. Mills.
  3 Are you very hungry? asked Mum.
  4 Stop that! shouted the caretaker.
  5 Be very quiet, whispered Michael.
  6 David asked, Have you seen my cricket bat?
  7 Please close the door, he said. Someone may hear us.
  8 Suddenly I stopped. I've forgotten my ticket, I said.
  9 Yes, shouted Bobby. It's mine.
10 It isn't fair, I cried. You cheated.
11 Hazel said, Aren't those roses beautiful?
12 Hazel said she couldn't stay, explained June.

B Write out these sentences putting in the speech marks ''_____'' and other necessary punctuation.

  1 That doesn't belong to me said Angus.
  2 Have you seen my dog Cathy asked.
  3 Try that coat on suggested the shop assistant.
  4 The old man looked very angry get out he yelled.
  5 That's not hard he boasted watch me do it.
  6 No Andrew the coach said you are not shooting first time.
  7 Alex asked me to watch him Stuart explained.
  8 Will you please carry this parcel for me begged the old woman.
  9 Where have you been I've been waiting an hour for you grumbled Roger.
10 The answer Mr. Rigby gave me was you can't come in with your shoes on.

Conjunctions

A Write out the **conjunctions** in each of these sentences.

1 The children played on the beach and went in the sea.
2 The cricket match was abandoned because it was raining.
3 We are moving to London if Dad can get a job.
4 You must have a ticket otherwise you won't get in.
5 Let's wait here until the bus comes.
6 Ian is not sure whether he can come with us.
7 We pulled at the door, but could not open it.
8 You need not stay unless you wish to.
9 Most people feel nervous when they visit the dentist.
10 Heather sprained her ankle so she cannot go to school.

B Use one of the **conjunctions** from the list to complete each of the sentences.

because	and	when	for	but	although
	until	since	wherever	while	

1 I am disappointed with her _____ she should know better.
2 We have stayed here _____ you left.
3 My knee is still swollen _____ I have rested it.
4 The faithful sheepdog followed the shepherd _____ he went.
5 Bob could not play football _____ he had sprained his ankle.
6 You clean the car _____ I take out the dog.
7 I was walking to the shops _____ I saw the accident.
8 We watched the strange object in the sky _____ we could see it no longer.
9 The sun shone again _____ the cricket match continued.
10 Jamie took the penalty for a second time _____ he missed again.

Vocabulary and spelling (2)

A Every word begins with **p**. Each pair in the bracket sounds alike.
Write out the words.

1 { when you have toothache you have   _____
{ a sheet of glass in a window   _____

2 { white or having a colourless face   _____
{ a bucket   _____

3 { animals' feet with claws   _____
{ to stop what you are doing for a moment   _____

4 { a flat fish which is good to eat   _____
{ somewhere; a spot or position   _____

B Every word begins with **r**. Each pair in the bracket sounds alike.

1 { the underground part of a plant   _____
{ a road or path from one place to another   _____

2 { lines of people or things   _____
{ a beautiful flower with a thorny stem   _____

3 { to lift up   _____
{ beams of light   _____

4 { you must be able to _____ to answer this   _____
{ a tall grass growing near water   _____

C Every word begins with **s**. Each pair in the bracket sounds alike.

1 { a male child   _____
{ the star that gives us heat and light   _____

2 { without a curve or a bend   _____
{ a narrow channel of sea   _____

3 { to plant seeds   _____
{ to use a needle and thread   _____

4 { a fence with a step on each side   _____
{ the manner in which you do something   _____

Mixed bag (3)

A Rewrite these sentences using **one word** in place of the words in bold type.

1 Elizabeth **kept out of the way of** Sally and Emma.
2 The window was broken **quite by accident**.
3 During the **great shortage of rain** the pond dried up.
4 My teacher told me that my work was **getting better**.
5 My friend is always **fair and truthful**.
6 At the sale the prices were **made less than before**.
7 The actor was **not able to be heard** at the back of the theatre.
8 Sarah's job at the supermarket is only **for the time being**.
9 Malcolm told me **over and over again** about his new bicycle.
10 The policeman dived into the canal **without waiting a second**.

B What do you call the place where

1 doctors see their patients? s_____
2 birds are kept? a_____
3 chickens are hatched? i_____
4 films are shown? c_____
5 TV programmes and films are produced? s_____

C Write the class name for each of these groups, then add an example of your own.

1 guitar, piano, drums, organ
2 bacon, beef, lamb, pork
3 squash, golf, football, cricket
4 yacht, trawler, tug, schooner
5 labrador, corgi, terrier, poodle
6 Mercury, Jupiter, Venus, Mars
7 green, orange, red, yellow
8 beech, ash, oak, sycamore
9 sweater, jeans, T shirt, skirt
10 table, settee, bed, chair

Occupations

A Write the names of the occupations shown in the pictures.

B Name the occupations of the people who sell

1 writing paper, envelopes, greeting cards.
2 papers and magazines.
3 screws, nails, hinges, tools.
4 medicines, ointments, cosmetics.
5 precious stones, rings, watches.
6 lamb, beef, pork, ham.
7 plaice, cod, mackerel, shrimps.
8 pies, cakes, bread, tarts.

C Name the occupation of the person who

1 looks after zoo animals.
2 grows flowers, shrubs and trees.
3 writes novels.
4 sells goods to the highest bidder.
5 repairs motor cars, motor cycles etc.
6 takes ships into and out of port.
7 carves statues.
8 treats corns and nails on the feet.

Apostrophe—possession

A Write the following using the apostrophe to show there is **one owner**.

1 the pencil belonging to Peter
2 the gun belonging to the soldier
3 the brush of the caretaker
4 the fields of the farmer
5 the spade belonging to Mr. Clark

6 the neck of the giraffe
7 the typewriter belonging to the
   secretary
8 the dinner of the dog
9 the feet of the duck
10 the pen belonging to Sally

B Write the following using the apostrophe to show that there is **more than one owner**.

1 the tents of the scouts
2 the trunks of the elephants
3 the petals belonging to the flowers
4 the submarine of the sailors
5 the room belonging to the
   teachers

6 the boots belonging to the
   footballers
7 the rocket of the astronauts
8 the wings of the birds
9 the club for pilots
10 a school for dancers

C Write the following using the apostrophe to show that there is **more than one owner**.

1 the helmets of the firemen
2 the radios belonging to the
   policemen
3 the dresses of the ladies
4 the clothes belonging to the
   babies
5 the gardens of the neighbours

6 the hideout of the thieves
7 the play area for children
8 the sister of the brothers
9 the animals owned by the zoos
10 the horns belonging to the oxen

D Use the apostrophe to show ownership.

1 the fleeces belonging to the sheep
2 the ears of the donkey
3 the masks of the frogmen

4 the feathers of the bird
5 the club belonging to the women
6 the wings belonging to the geese

Vocabulary and spelling (3)

A The answers to these clues all end in **cious**.

1 very valuable   — — — — c i o u s
2 most pleasant to eat   — — — — — c i o u s
3 plenty of room   — — — — c i o u s
4 doubting whether something is true   — — — — — — c i o u s
5 not knowing what is going on around you   — — — — — — — c i o u s

B The answers all have **ll** in them.

1 precious stones, gold, rings   j_____
2 10 make a centimetre   m_____
3 grub from which a butterfly or moth comes   c_____
4 piece of land used as an extra garden   a_____
5 the same distance apart all along   p_____

C These answers all end in **ible**.

1 cannot be done   i_____
2 unable to be seen   i_____
3 showing good sense; wise   s_____
4 can be reversed   r_____
5 Who is r_____ for this excellent work?

D These answers all begin with **ch**.

1 when Jesus Christ's birth is celebrated   Ch_____
2 a person who is paid to drive a car   ch_____
3 a large tree; its nut is called a conker   ch_____
4 a stage in the life of an insect   ch_____
5 someone who treats feet   ch_____

Punctuation

A Rewrite these sentences, using **capital letters** where necessary.

1 tom played squash with terry on monday night.
2 when marjorie visited london she went in the houses of parliament.
3 every christmas peter stays with his aunty edna in nairobi.
4 britain imports jamaican sugar, new zealand apples and australian wool.
5 the busy holiday months in england are july and august.
6 pelé, the famous footballer, played for santos f.c. in brazil and new york cosmos.
7 janet's sister, emma, is studying french at sydney university.
8 in 1978 queen elizabeth II opened the commonwealth games in edmonton, alberta, canada.

B Write out these sentences putting in **commas**, **full stops**, **question marks** and **exclamation marks** where necessary.

1 Morag Sally and I went for a walk
2 The cyclist after a brief stop for food resumed the race
3 "If you see him will you ask him to write"
4 Some common metals are copper lead iron and zinc
5 Grandad after a big dinner went to sleep
6 "Quick march" yelled the drill-sergeant
7 "Are you feeling better today" asked the teacher
8 "What do you think you are doing" shouted the angry farmer

C Write in full these abbreviated words.

| 1 he'll | 3 couldn't | 5 I'm | 7 they've |
| 2 she's | 4 won't | 6 you're | 8 who's |

D Write these words in abbreviated form.

| 1 they are | 3 she cannot | 5 he shall not | 7 they will |
| 2 you would | 4 that is | 6 where is | 8 where have |

Mixed bag (4)

A Give the meanings of these **abbreviations**.

1 PTO	**5** RSPCA	**9** a.m.	**13** RN	**17** JP
2 PC	**6** GC	**10** GMT	**14** e.g.	**18** VIP
3 BC	**7** lbw	**11** m	**15** etc.	**19** EU
4 Feb.	**8** Ave.	**12** kph	**16** BBC	**20** ITV

B Write the missing **proper adjectives**.

1 cars made in Britain _____ cars

2 apples grown in Canada _____ apples

3 peaches from Australia _____ peaches

4 bananas grown in Jamaica _____ bananas

5 coffee from Kenya _____ coffee

6 bacon from Denmark _____ bacon

7 watches made in Switzerland _____ watches

8 timber from Finland _____ timber

9 bulbs from Holland _____ bulbs

C Write the **sound** words.

1 the _____ of brakes

2 the _____ of rusty hinges

3 the _____ of an explosion

4 the _____ of a drum

5 the _____ of leaves

6 the _____ of thunder

D Write the animal **sounds**.

1 frogs _____

2 owls _____

3 dogs _____

4 pigs _____

5 horses _____

6 sheep _____

7 monkeys _____

8 cows _____

Vocabulary—similar meanings

A Choose one of the words in the list in place of a word or words in bold type in the sentences below.

pester	vivid	errors	dilute	various	constantly
exterior	vacant	request	extinguish	surrender	glorious

 1 The machine worked **without stopping** for twenty hours.
 2 You should **water down** the orange juice.
 3 The firemen worked hard to **put out** the flames.
 4 The painters have nearly finished the **outside** of our house.
 5 "Don't **bother** me now. I'm too busy," said Francis.
 6 You must **apply for** permission to alter your house.
 7 There are **assorted** kinds of sweets in the tin.
 8 What a **splendid** display of roses!
 9 The brave soldiers were determined not to **give themselves up**.
10 Tom used **very bright** colours in his paintings.
11 The old house was **unoccupied** for years.
12 You have made too many **mistakes** in your work.

B Here are twenty-four words which you can arrange into twelve pairs. The words of each pair will have similar meanings.
    Use your dictionary to help you to write them in pairs.

pull	guard	floating	crush
grind	polite	disappear	feeble
defend	amaze	haul	genuine
useless	buoyant	sincere	force
weak	compel	support	futile
encourage	courteous	astound	vanish

Singular and plural

A Write these sentences in the **plural** form.

1 The boy has read his book.
2 I am going near Oban for my holiday.
3 The footballer wears a red jersey.
4 I shall sell it to the girl.
5 The girl tripped over the stone and hurt herself.
6 The play wasn't very well acted.
7 I must help to feed the monkey.
8 The man was very tired after he had worked hard in the garden.
9 I saw a goose in the field.
10 This boy wishes to play chess.

B Write these sentences in the **singular** form.

1 Our friends came on holiday with us.
2 The policemen checked their watches before they set off.
3 The knives have been sharpened.
4 Some women shouted at us.
5 Firemen wear uniforms.
6 "Have you seen them?" we asked.
7 Chimpanzees are very intelligent animals.
8 The first chapters of the books were missing.
9 We are sure you do not understand these ideas.
10 We were pleased with the examination results which were published in the papers yesterday.

Adverbs (3)

A Complete these sentences by using **verbs** and **adverbs** so that the second sentence has the same meaning as the first. The first one is done for you.

1 My friend is a careful driver.   My friend drives carefully.
2 Joan gave a quick answer.   Joan _____ .
3 We are all sound sleepers.   We _____ .
4 Sam is a slow reader.   Sam _____ .
5 The other team were bad losers.   The other team _____ .
6 The bright sun shines on the beach.   The sun _____ .
7 The explorer made an interesting speech.   The explorer _____ .
8 Darren is a strong swimmer.   Darren _____ .
9 The secretary sent a prompt answer.   The secretary _____ .
10 Pelé was a skilful player.   Pelé _____ .

B Rewrite these sentences, by using **one adverb** in place of the words in heavy type.

1 The monk copied the manuscript **with great care**.
2 The electric cables were not joined **in the correct way**.
3 Sensible people visit their dentist **at regular times**.
4 The burglar entered the house **without making a sound**.
5 The two space ships docked **exactly on time**.
6 The kind man gave **a lot of money** to the lifeboat fund.
7 Jasmine asked the question **in a polite way**.
8 **In the end** the battered ship managed to reach land.
9 The artist looked **with pride** at his latest painting.
10 Derek worked out all the problems **in his head**.

AVALANCHE

Brachen was crammed to overflowing. Travellers from the long-distance trains held up by the snowfall filled the hotels. Evacuees from the threatened mountain villages were billeted on private families. The large waiting rooms next to the station restaurant had been cleared to receive refugees. The proprietor of the restaurant, who normally did a thriving business, had handed over his kitchen and his coffee machines to the Red Cross and his staff were working as volunteers.

The wireless had been moved to the left luggage department, where it was kept turned on all day, so that anyone who wanted to could listen to the latest reports on what was happening in the threatened districts.

In the early morning light the long platform stretched away, lonely and deserted. No express trains stopped there now for a few bustling minutes before speeding away again. Everything looked grey: the rails, the dirty snow, the trucks in the siding and the long green Lucerne–Rome express, which had been standing for eight hours and thirty-two minutes, waiting for the signal to move.

A few railwaymen in blue overalls and black caps moved about. Now and then the sound of lowing came from one of the cattle trucks that stood in a siding under the broad station roof. The heads of three white oxen with great dewlaps gazed out mildly through an opening. The heavy snow-ploughs stood in another siding. Two soldiers in overalls were working on them.

At seven the wireless began to give the first news bulletins. A little group of evacuees and three of the station officials gathered in front of the left luggage office. People with pale sleepy faces climbed down out of the waiting train and joined them.

The Pestalozzi boys straggled out of the warm, stuffy waiting room into the clear, frosty morning outside. Paolo, with his black curls standing on end, was yawning his head off. As soon as they saw the group on the platform and heard the familiar voice of the announcer, they came rushing along to listen. All except Werner, who trailed along behind them with his hands in his pockets and a reluctant expression on his face.

Reproduced by kind permission of Hodder & Stoughton Children's Books
From *Avalanche* by A. Rutgers Van Der Loeff

1 Give two reasons why Brachen was filled to overflowing.
2 Name the two cities the green express connected.
3 What was the time of the first news bulletin?
4 Why weren't any express trains calling at Brachen?
5 What uniform was worn by the railwaymen?
6 Describe the weather that particular morning.
7 Name two kinds of railway equipment kept round the station.
8 Give two reasons why the proprietor of the restaurant was a 'good' man.
9 Why was the wireless moved to the left luggage office?
10 How do you know Paolo was half asleep?
11 Where do you think this disaster took place?
12 Find the words in the passage that mean
   a messages.   e owner.
   b successful.   f giving services freely.
   c unwilling.   g crowded.
   d radio.   h people moved because of danger.
13 For you to find out:
   a Who began the Red Cross? When? Where? Why?
   b What are Pestalozzi Children's Villages?
   c What are dewlaps?

Adjectives (2)

Complete the following sentences using **adjectives** formed from the nouns in the brackets.

A 1 The children were _____ after playing in the hot sun. (thirst)
2 Grandad was very _____ after weeding the garden. (sleep)
3 The small boat was tossed about in the _____ sea. (storm)
4 The cricket match was spoiled because of the _____ weather. (shower)

B 1 The _____ water will kill the fish. (ice)
2 Let's sit in this _____ part of the park. (shade)
3 It's too _____ to see the yachts in the bay. (haze)
4 The cactus is a _____ plant. (prickle)

C 1 Have you read Paula's _____ poem? (fun)
2 I'm not walking along that _____ path. (mud)
3 The chinchilla is a _____ animal. (fur)
4 Your recorder makes a _____ noise. (tin)

D 1 Look at that _____ puppy. (mischief)
2 My friend is a _____ footballer. (skill)
3 Mrs. Long wears _____ jewellery. (expense)
4 A steeplejack has a _____ job. (danger)

E Form **adjectives** from the following nouns.

1 haste	**6** poison	**11** nature
2 leak	**7** circle	**12** expense
3 skin	**8** juice	**13** sun
4 wool	**9** accident	**14** sympathy
5 anger	**10** death	**15** depth

A   One word for several

Rewrite the following sentences, replacing the words in bold type by one word only.

1 The **people who lived next door** were very helpful when Mum was ill.
2 Tom kept his model railway in the **room where he slept**.
3 Sally walked along the corridor **without making a noise**.
4 At the airport our family joined the long **line of waiting people**.
5 My **mother's brother** often comes fishing with us.
6 The teacher said she had not **made up her mind** whether to have the match.
7 Joan said that she had started to write her **own life story**.
8 Our electric meter is read **once every three months**.
9 There was a **general shortage of food** in the land after the earthquake.
10 If you heat a piece of steel it will **get bigger**.

B   Incorrect sentences

Rewrite the following sentences correctly.

1 Jamie played football with Peter and I.
2 Mr. Peacock is headmaster of a girl's school.
3 The cat was run over with a car.
4 I'll share the sweets between Heather, Paul and Elizabeth.
5 Look at the baby drinking from it's bottle.
6 Sam is nearly twelve months older than me.
7 Alan, Bob and Bill was sheltering from the storm.
8 I have earned less house marks this term.
9 "I didn't do nothing wrong," sobbed Mark.
10 Our teacher said he would learn me to dive in the pool.
11 Frank is the tallest of the two boys.
12 None of the pencils are sharp.

A Forming verbs from nouns

Complete these sentences by filling in the blanks with **verbs** formed from the nouns in brackets.

1 The results of the art competition were _____ at assembly. (announcement)
2 They _____ to choose a new goalkeeper.   (decision)
3 Every swimmer _____ the skill of Mark Spitz.   (admiration)
4 Dr. Livingstone _____ the Victoria Falls in Africa.   (discovery)
5 We were _____ to learn that the fishermen were safe.   (relief)
6 The elephants were _____ by the keeper.   (food)
7 I hope the divers _____ the lost treasure ship.   (discovery)
8 Janet said she would _____ ten friends to her party.   (invitation)
9 When we have more rain the grass will _____ .   (growth)
10 You will _____ more if you read more.   (knowledge)

B Forming nouns from verbs

Complete these sentences by filling in the blanks with **nouns** formed from the verbs in brackets.

1 Crowds greeted the _____ of the pop star.   (arrive)
2 The children's _____ at the concert was excellent.   (behave)
3 The _____ was blocked by fallen bricks.   (enter)
4 Janice suffered a painful _____ when she fell on the ice.   (injure)
5 The audience applauded the _____ of the orchestra.   (perform)
6 We had a large _____ of groceries.   (deliver)
7 We were five kilometres away but heard the _____ .   (explode)
8 The general expected _____ from all his soldiers.   (obey)
9 Professor Brytor's _____ will help the farmers.   (invent)
10 The referee's _____ is always final.   (decide)

Mixed bag (5)

A Odd one out
Write out the word in each group which does not fit in with the others.

1 talk, listen, say, tell, speak, utter, remark
2 aged, antique, modern, elderly, ancient, old
3 home, flat, residence, dwelling, school, house
4 fast, quick, rapid, early, swift, speedy
5 small, tiny, minute, little, hole, wee, puny
6 great, huge, vast, immense, square, enormous
7 bold, fearless, cautious, adventurous, daring
8 tutor, scholar, student, pupil, learner
9 dark, gloomy, dismal, dreary, deadly, sombre
10 collect, gather, assemble, amass, accumulate, scatter
11 seize, loosen, grasp, clutch, clasp, clench
12 dash, rush, hurry, loiter, scurry, scoot

B Opposites
Write the opposites of the following words.

1 cowardly   4 thoughtless   7 horizontal
2 regular   5 gentle   8 reckless
3 gigantic   6 peculiar   9 abundant

C Rhyming words
Write out the word that rhymes with the word in bold type.

1 **plate**	meat	plait	weight	pleat
2 **sane**	scene	rein	wine	green
3 **fetch**	bleach	batch	clutch	stretch
4 **foul**	fool	howl	bowl	four
5 **port**	pour	part	court	hurt
6 **suite**	suit	sure	soot	beat
7 **field**	healed	felled	fooled	farmed
8 **meant**	mean	stint	tent	meal

Vocabulary and spelling (4)

A The answers to these clues have either **ei** or **ie** in them.

1 the daughter of your brother or sister   n _ _ _ _ _
2 a piece of cloth for wiping your nose
   h _ _ _ _ _ _ _ _ _ _ _
3 the roof of a room   c _ _ _ _ _ _ _
4 someone who steals   t _ _ _ _ _
5 to think that something is true   b _ _ _ _ _ _ _
6 to have something given to you   r _ _ _ _ _ _ _
7 part of something   p _ _ _ _ _
8 someone you like; a pal   f _ _ _ _ _ _
9 to mislead or cheat   d _ _ _ _ _ _ _
10 how tall a thing is   h _ _ _ _ _ _

B These answers all have **y** in them.

1 a machine for making electricity   d_____
2 a machine with keys worked by the fingers   t_____
3 a sweet-smelling spring flower   h_____
4 an African wild animal like a dog   h_____
5 a high explosive   d_____
6 a very large snake   p_____

C These answers all end in **or**.

1 an imaginary line around the Earth's centre   _____or
2 a moving staircase   _____or
3 one who writes a book   _____or
4 someone who watches a game, a show, etc.   _____or
5 a passage-way   _____or
6 a machine for showing films on a screen   _____or

Direct and indirect speech

A   Change these sentences to **indirect speech**. Look at this example.

Dad said, "We'll miss the bus."   (direct speech)
Dad said that we would miss the bus.   (indirect speech)

1 Brian said, "I'm tired after that long walk."
2 The caretaker said, "I've lost my big brush".
3 "I've lost my keys," said the teacher.
4 "Has anyone found a bunch of keys?" asked the teacher.
5 "You can stay a little longer," suggested Eric.
6 "Try harder," my dad advised, "or you'll never finish the job."
7 "Have you seen a black and white kitten?" the old lady asked.
8 "You musn't play near the river, Bill," warned his friend.
9 He said, "I used to play for the first team."
10 "I am sure," said Mr. Thomas, "that you haven't listened."

B   Change these sentences from indirect to **direct speech**.

e.g. The girl said she was tired.   (indirect)
    The girl said, "I am tired."   (direct)

1 The boys said they were very sorry for being late.
2 Mum said that dinner was ready.
3 The pilot remarked that it may be a bumpy flight.
4 Tom said that he would not be able to play.
5 Dora asked if I was going to town.
6 The secretary said that the paper was hers.
7 The teacher said that she wouldn't be away long.
8 The farmer explained that he was going to dig some drains.
9 The boy asked Mr. Aitken if he would return his football.
10 I asked Mr. Perkins where he would be going in August.

Comprehension (2)

BATS

I had reached a deep ravine in the great limestone rocks of Somerset. There are dozens of caverns and most of them afford a shelter for bats of six or seven different species. Horseshoe Bats are abundant. Like the huge chrysalids of some exotic butterfly, they hang from the walls of the caverns, still, silent, and torpid. But shine an electric torch on their dusky bodies or breathe ever so lightly on them and they flex their legs and draw themselves up tightly to the rock. They are profoundly asleep.

In these caverns lives the handsome Natterer's Bat, a pretty creature with long, almost transparent ears. Its underside is a soft white, very noticeable when the bat is on the wing. In fact among some country-folk this species has been dubbed the "White-waistcoat Bat". Another species, known as the Whiskered Bat, also inhabits the same caves. It has a goblin-like expression and its fur is grizzled chestnut above and dusky beneath. Both these bats are difficult to capture, for they wedge themselves deep in the crevices.

With luck a Long-eared Bat may be found here. Its enormous ears are as long as its body. Its piteous eyes stand out like beads. Why has this species got such long ears? Perhaps because it hunts at night when insects are scarce.

The rarest of the bats inhabiting these caves is the Barbastelle. One April I could plainly see one with its curiously formed ears, its evil-looking face and black shining eyes, as my electric torch revealed it in the depths of a narrow crevice. For a few minutes it defied me from its fastness, squeaking in a querulous manner. Finally it crept out of sight, crying its protest until its voice faded away into a deep, metallic buzz.

Reproduced by kind permission of The Hamlyn Publishing Group Ltd. from *The Countryman Book* (originally published by Odhams Press Ltd.)

1 Give the names of all the different kinds of bats found by the writer.
2 Which was the most common bat he found?
3 Which bat was the most difficult to capture? Why?
4 What do bats feed on?
5 Describe, in your own words, the type of sleep enjoyed by Horseshoe Bats.
6 Which bat makes a 'metallic buzz' sound?
7 What is the main difference between the appearance of a Whiskered Bat and a Natterer's Bat?
8 What are chrysalids? Why are they compared with bats?
9 Which was the rarest bat found in the caverns?
10 Find the words in the passage that mean
   a very deeply.
   b sort or kind.
   c not moving.
   d made known.
   e lives in.
   f named.
   g very sad.
   h allow or permit.
   i very plentiful.
   j easily seen through.

Mixed bag (6)

Rearrange these groups of letters to make names of the following.

A Zoo animals

1 NOIL   3 EFIGRFA   5 ALEMC

2 OKEMYN   4 BAZER   6 NOAOGRKA

B Vegetables

1 AEP   3 NNOOI   5 NIRTUP

2 OOTTAP   4 OTCRAR   6 AEBBCGA

C Trees

1 SAH   3 NEIP   5 ARCDE

2 KOA   4 ECBHE   6 HSTUCTEN

D Choose the correct **prefix** from the list below to form opposite meanings to these twelve words.

1 correct	5 wrap	9 fortunate
2 possible	6 convenient	10 experienced
3 regular	7 comfortable	11 comfort
4 obedient	8 polite	12 responsible

ir_____   un_____   dis_____

    im_____   in_____

E Rewrite the following sentences by choosing the correct form of the word in brackets.

1 Edwin is the _____ of the two boys.   (tall)

2 Sheila is the _____ swimmer in the school.   (fast)

3 Prince is the _____ horse in the race.   (young)

4 Terry is the _____ of the three boys.   (strong)

5 The lounge is the _____ of the two rooms.   (warm)

6 Tom Bunter is the _____ of the boys in the school.   (fat)

7 Our school is _____ than Kimwood High.   (large)

8 Do you think Sam is a _____ runner than Darren?   (good)

Answers

Page 2 Nouns

A **1** dog, field **2** bananas, custard, dish **3** elephants, logs **4** wine, grapes **5** policeman, cars, lorries **6** children, teachers, circus **7** lifeguard, swimmer **8** night, Tom, book, walk **9** porridge, bacon, egg, toast, breakfast **10** helicopter, football field, school
B **1** cuckoo **2** ceiling **3** concrete **4** cider **5** customer **6** cousin **7** crane **8** cheese **9** calendar **10** caterpillar

Page 3 Adjectives (1)

A **1** damp, foggy **2** blind, wooden **3** short, fat, tall, slim **4** large, powerful, striped **5** small, strong, rough **6** slender, long, short **7** fast, thrilling, large **8** thick, blue, red, woollen **9** extinct, flightless, giant **10** brave, exhausted, dangerous, hot, humid
B **1** priceless **2** fatal **3** fierce **4** fragrant **5** empty **6** huge **7** courageous **8** victorious **9** difficult **10** nourishing
C Check your child's sentences.

Page 4 Verbs (1)

A **1** slipped, fell **2** finished, returned **3** ate, ran **4** took, make **5** fed, cleaned **6** baked, cleaned, washed **7** saw, rescue **8** sped, braked, skidded **9** climbed, checked **10** fell, broke
B **1** measured **2** collided **3** swooped **4** perched **5** collapsed **6** flickered **7** shattered **8** repeated **9** interrupted **10** marooned
C Check your child's use of verbs in his/her sentences.

Page 5 Adverbs (1)

A **1** swiftly **2** loudly **3** brightly **4** comfortably **5** annually **6** wearily **7** slowly, quickly **8** clearly **9** suddenly, cleverly **10** immediately, late
B **1** correctly **2** foolishly **3** soundly **4** frantically **5** fiercely **6** briefly **7** silently **8** anxiously **9** tunefully **10** bitterly
C Check your child's use of adverbs in his/her sentences.

Page 6 Alphabetical order

A bicycle, comb, duck , hammer, kite, pig
B **1** beach, cage, hobby, meat, runway, warrior
2 acorn, grass, nylon, quiz, smell, white
3 cry, duck, frost, jelly, puzzle, vein
C sailor, seesaw, shark, skeleton, spear, star
D **1** path, pea, pier, potato, prize, public
2 bed, bite, black, boat, bread, bulb
3 wasp, weak, whip, witch, worm, wrist
E cactus, cake, camera, caravan, castle, catapult
F **1** spade, speak, spin, spoon, spun, spy
2 price, pride, prime, princess, prison, prize
3 chain, chalk, chameleon, channel, chart, chatter

Page 7 Sentences

A **1** The man is putting his hat **on his head.**
2 Dad is wearing a watch **on his wrist.**
3 Sam is painting **the back door.**
4 It was raining heavily **so Jean put up her umbrella.**
5 The train is stopping **at the signal.**
6 Nicky is cutting bread **with a knife.**
7 The jumbo jet is landing **at Manchester Airport.**
8 The lifeboat is speeding **to rescue the sailors.**
B **1 – 5** Check that your child's chosen words are suitable.
C **1 – 5** Check that your child's chosen words are suitable.

Page 8 Compound words

A **1** head + light = headlight
2 post + card = postcard

3 life + belt = lifebelt
4 air + plane = airplane
5 foot + print = footprint
6 sun + dial = sundial
7 fire + man = fireman
8 hand + cuff = handcuff
9 hedge + hog = hedgehog
10 snow + flake = snowflake
11 bed + room = bedroom
12 wood + pecker = woodpecker
B Check that your child's answers are compound words.

Page 9 Vocabulary and spelling (1)
A ice, cafe, elephant, library, alphabet, nightmare, dandelion = Iceland
B bulldozer, ancient, dodge, glacier, eagle, ranch = badger
C August, pork, rich, infant, customer, octopus, triangle = apricot

Page 10 Singular and plural
1 horse – horses 2 tooth – teeth
3 piano – pianos 4 man – men 5 star – stars 6 foot – feet 7 baby – babies
8 bus – buses 9 monkey – monkeys
10 leaf – leaves 11 volcano – volcanoes
12 sheep – sheep 13 mousetrap – mousetraps 14 oasis – oases
15 tree – trees

Page 11 Mixed bag (1)
A 1 thin **2** closed **3** four **4** married
5 pretty **6** rude **7** imaginary
8 permanent **9** failure **10** private
B 1 – 10 Check that your child's words have a similar meaning to those written.
C 1 Football **2** Rugby **3** Netball
4 Cricket **5** Squash **6** Swimming
7 Hockey **8** Tennis **9** Angling
10 Badminton

Page 12 Gender
A 1 grandfather **2** steward **3** peacock
4 manager **5** horse **6** headmaster
7 boar **8** duke **9** monk

B 1 actress **2** hind **3** lady **4** spinster
5 female **6** filly **7** widow **8** mother-in-law **9** queen
C 1 wizard/witch **2** waiter/waitress
3 mayor/mayoress **4** groom/bride
5 stag/hind

Page 13 Picture story
Check that your child's story describes what is happening in the pictures.

Page 14 Verbs (2)
Past tense
A 1 shook **2** held **3** sprang **4** struck
5 wrote **6** stopped **7** thought, was
8 drove, found, were **9** went, had
10 bled, fell
Past participle
B 1 known **2** gone **3** swollen **4** hidden
5 written **6** eaten, frozen **7** fallen, flown **8** beaten, lost **9** grown, fed
10 mown, trimmed

Page 15 Homonyms
A 2a key **b** quay **3a** mayor **b** mare
4a mussel **b** muscle **5a** yolk **b** yoke
6a leek **b** leak **7a** buoy **b** boy **8a** peer **b** pier
B Check that your child's sentences include the nouns given in Question A.

Page 16 Rhyming words
A 1 much, such **2** raw **3** loose, noose
4 low, sew **5** caught, sought
6 unkempt, cement **7** growth **8** bowl, foal **9** near, deer **10** dove, above
B 1 stain **2** mood **3** rein **4** cheer
5 yacht **6** chased **7** agree **8** crumb
9 sow **10** purse

Page 17 Prepositions
Check that your child's sentences describe the relevant picture and include the correct preposition from the box.

Page 18 Direct speech (1)
A 1 Where are my slippers

2 Come to my house on Saturday morning
3 You're late
4 Yes
5 Paul said he was very hungry
6 Stop looking....I've found it
7 Washington is the capital of the USA
8 Penalty
9 Good morning....You're up early
10 Try to write an interesting story, Jenny
11 Today has been a happy day....Not for me though....I've lost my purse
12 I was asleep....The thunder woke me up. I'm frightened. Please come and talk to me.
B 1 – 6 Check your child's answers.

Page 19 Verbs (3)
A 1 – 12 Check that your child has used a suitable verb to complete the sentences.
B 1 unwrap **2** learn **3** hurry **4** destroy **5** slide **6** rescue **7** scatter **8** guard **9** repeat **10** wriggle

Page 20 Better words
A, B and C Check that your child's chosen words are suitable for each sentence.

Page 21 Adverbs (2)
A 1 – 12 Check that your child's chosen adverbs are suitable for each sentence.
B 1 – 12 Check that your child's sentences use the given verbs and adverbs suitably.

Page 22 Collective nouns
A 1 army **2** library **3** swarm **4** staff **5** pack **6** flight **7** suite **8** collection or album **9** anthology **10** school
B 1 singing **2** working on a ship **3** enjoying themselves **4** rioting **5** playing music **6** judging **7** waiting **8** dancing
C 2 wolves – pack **3** tools – set

4 footballers – team **5** ships – fleet **6** bananas – bunch

Page 23 Mixed bag (2)
A 1 passed **2** past **3** past **4** passed **5** past **6** passed **7** past **8** past **9** past **10** past
B 1 moon **2** owl **3** foot **4** cloth **5** late **6** dog
C 1 fallen **2** is **3** lying **4** sung **5** eaten **6** spoken **7** missed **8** ever **9** anything **10** teaching

Page 24 Pronouns
A 1 him **2** me, she **3** us, we **4** We, him **5** he, her **6** you, them **7** them, they **8** You, you, his **9** his, it **10** us, our
B 1 him **2** she, her **3** he, him **4** they, it **5** she, them **6** them, her **7** she, her, he **8** he, him, them **9** they, her **10** he, us

Page 25 Similes
A 1 as wise as an owl **2** as cunning as a fox **3** as slow as a tortoise **4** as agile as a monkey **5** as busy as a bee **6** as graceful as a swan **7** as slippery as an eel **8** as brave as a lion
B 1 bat **2** pancake **3** mouse **4** peacock **5** lark **6** rake
C 1 old boots **2** bone **3** gold **4** mustard **5** honey **6** ice **7** clean **8** alike **9** cool **10** black **11** burnt **12** regular

Page 26 Direct speech (2)
A 1 "I am going home," said Mark.
2 "Bring my books, please," said Mr. Mills.
3 "Are you hungry?" asked Mum.
4 "Stop that!" shouted the caretaker.
5 "Be very quiet," whispered Michael.
6 David asked, "Have you seen my cricket bat?"
7 "Please close the door," he said. "Someone may hear us."
8 Suddenly I stopped. "I've forgotten my ticket," I said.

9 "Yes," shouted Bobby. "It's mine."
10 "It isn't fair," I cried. "You cheated."
11 Hazel said, "Aren't those roses beautiful?"
12 "Hazel said she couldn't stay," explained June.
B 1 "That doesn't belong to me," said Angus.
2 "Have you seen my dog?" Cathy asked.
3 "Try that coat on," suggested the shop assistant.
4 The old man looked very angry, "Get out!" he yelled.
5 "That's not hard!" he boasted, "Watch me do it."
6 "No Andrew," the coach said. "You are not shooting first time."
7 "Alex asked me to watch him," Stuart explained.
8 "Will you please carry this parcel for me?" begged the old woman.
9 "Where have you been? I've been waiting an hour for you," grumbled Roger.
10 The answer Mr. Rigby gave me was, "You can't come in with your shoes on."

Page 27 Conjunctions

A 1 and 2 because 3 if 4 otherwise
5 until 6 whether 7 but 8 unless
9 when 10 so
B 1 because 2 since 3 although
4 wherever 5 since 6 while 7 when
8 until 9 and 10 but

Page 28 Vocabulary and spelling (2)

A 1 pain/pane 2 pale/pail
3 paws/pause 4 plaice/place
B 1 root/route 2 rows/rose 3 raise/rays
4 read/reed
C 1 son/sun 2 straight/strait 3 sow/sew
4 stile/style

Page 29 Mixed bag (3)

A The following words are possible answers. Check your child's answers and accept anything that has the same meaning as the word in bold.
1 avoided 2 accidentally 3 drought
4 improving 5 honest 6 reduced
7 inaudible 8 temporary 9 repeatedly
10 immediately
B 1 surgery 2 aviary 3 incubator
4 cinema 5 studio
C 1 musical instrument (plus your child's own addition)
2 meat (plus your child's own addition)
3 ball game (plus your child's own addition)
4 boat (plus your child's own addition)
5 dog (plus your child's own addition)
6 planet (plus your child's own addition)
7 colour (plus your child's own addition)
8 tree (plus your child's own addition)
9 clothes (plus your child's own addition)
10 furniture (plus your child's own addition)

Page 30 Occupations

A 1 chef 2 artist 3 optician 4 jockey
5 conductor 6 librarian 7 dentist
8 steeplejack 9 decorator
B 1 stationer 2 newsagent
3 ironmonger 4 chemist 5 jeweller
6 butcher 7 fishmonger 8 baker
C 1 zookeeper 2 gardener 3 author
4 auctioneer 5 mechanic 6 pilot
7 sculptor 8 chiropodist

Page 31 Apostrophe – possession

A 1 Peter's pencil 2 the soldier's gun
3 the caretaker's brush 4 the farmer's field 5 Mr. Clark's spade 6 the giraffe's neck 7 the secretary's typewriter 8 the dog's dinner 9 the duck's feet 10 Sally's pen

B **1** the scouts' tents **2** the elephants' trunks **3** the flowers' petals **4** the sailors' submarine **5** the teachers' room **6** the footballers' boots **7** the astronauts' rocket **8** the birds' wings **9** the pilots' club **10** a dancers' school
C **1** the firemen's helmets **2** the policemen's radios **3** the ladies' dresses **4** the babies' clothes **5** the neighbours' gardens **6** the thieves' hideout **7** the children's play area **8** the brothers' sister **9** the zoos' animals **10** the oxen's horn
D **1** the sheep's fleeces **2** the donkey's ear **3** the frogmen's masks **4** the bird's feathers **5** the women's club **6** the geese's wings

Page 32 Vocabulary and spelling (3)
A **1** precious **2** delicious **3** spacious **4** suspicious **5** unconscious
B **1** jewellery **2** millimetre **3** caterpillar **4** allotment **5** parallel
C **1** impossible **2** invisible **3** sensible **4** reversible **5** responsible
D **1** Christmas **2** chauffeur **3** chestnut **4** chrysalis **5** chiropodist

Page 33 Punctuation
A **1** Tom played squash with Terry on Monday night.
2 When Marjorie visited London she went in the Houses of Parliament.
3 Every Christmas Peter stays with his Aunty Edna in Nairobi.
4 Britain imports Jamaican sugar, New Zealand apples and Australian wool.
5 The busy holiday months in England are July and August.
6 Pelé, the famous footballer, played for Santos F.C. in Brazil and New York Cosmos.
7 Janet's sister, Emma, is studying French at Sydney University.
8 In 1978 Queen Elizabeth II opened the Commonwealth Games in Edmonton, Alberta, Canada.
B **1** Morag, Sally and I went for a walk.
2 The cyclist, after a brief stop for food, resumed the race.
3 "If you see him, will you ask him to write?"
4 Some common metals are copper, lead, iron and zinc.
5 Grandad, after a big dinner, went to sleep.
6 "Quick, march!" yelled the drill-sergeant.
7 "Are you feeling better today?" asked the teacher.
8 "What do you think you are doing?" shouted the angry farmer.
C **1** he will **2** she is **3** could not **4** will not **5** I am **6** you are **7** they have **8** who is
D **1** they're **2** you'd **3** she can't **4** that's **5** he shan't **6** where's **7** they'll **8** where've

Page 34 Mixed bag (4)
A **1** Please Turn Over **2** Police Constable **3** Before Christ **4** February **5** The Royal Society for the Prevention of Cruelty to Animals **6** George Cross **7** leg before wicket **8** Avenue **9** before noon **10** Greenwich Mean Time **11** miles **12** kilometres per hour **13** Royal Navy **14** for example **15** and other things **16** British Broadcasting Corporation **17** Justice of the Peace **18** Very Important Person **19** European Union **20** Independent Television
B **1** British **2** Canadian **3** Australian **4** Jamaican **5** Kenyan **6** Danish **7** Swiss **8** Finish **9** Dutch
C **1** screech **2** squeak **3** bang **4** beat **5** rustle **6** clap
D **1** croak **2** hoot **3** bark **4** grunt **5** neigh **6** bleat **7** chatter **8** low

Page 35 Vocabulary – similar meanings

A 1 constantly **2** dilute **3** extinguish
4 exterior **5** pester **6** request **7** various
8 glorious **9** surrender **10** vivid
11 vacant **12** errors
B pull/haul, grind/crush, defend/guard,
useless/futile, weak/feeble,
encourage/support, polite/courteous,
amaze/astound, buoyant/floating,
compel/force, disappear/vanish,
sincere/genuine

Page 36 Singular and plural

A 1 The boys have read their books.
2 We are going near Oban for our
holidays.
3 The footballers wear red jerseys.
4 We shall sell them to the girls.
5 The girls tripped over the stones and
hurt themselves.
6 The plays weren't very well acted.
7 We must help to feed the monkeys.
8 The men were very tired after they
had worked hard in the gardens.
9 I saw geese in the fields.
10 These boys wish to play chess.
B 1 My friend came on holiday with me.
2 The policeman checked his watch
before he set off.
3 The knife had been sharpened.
4 A woman shouted at me.
5 The fireman wears a uniform.
6 "Have you seen him?" I asked.
7 The chimpanzee is a very intelligent
animal.
8 The first chapter of the book was
missing.
9 I am sure you do not understand this
idea.
10 I was pleased with the examination
result which was published in the paper
yesterday.

Page 37 Adverbs (3)

A 2 Joan answers quickly.
3 We sleep soundly.
4 Sam reads slowly.
5 The other team lost badly.
6 The sun shines brightly.
7 The explorer spoke interestingly.
8 Darren swims strongly.
9 The secretary answered promptly.
10 Pelé played skilfully.
B 1 carefully **2** correctly **3** regularly
4 silently **5** promptly **6** generously
7 politely **8** finally **9** proudly
10 mentally

Page 38 Comprehension (1)

1 Brachen was overflowing because of
the travellers and evacuees.
2 The green express connected Lucerne
and Rome.
3 The time for the first news bulletin
was seven.
4 Express trains weren't calling at
Brachen because the Lucerne-Rome
express train was stuck, waiting for the
signal to change.
5 The railwaymen wore black overalls
and black caps as uniforms.
6 The weather that particular morning
was grey.
7 Two kinds of railway equipment kept
round the station were cattle trucks and
snow-ploughs.
8 The proprietor of the restaurant was a
'good' man because he handed his
kitchen and coffee machine over to the
Red Cross and let his employees work
as volunteers.
9 The wireless was moved so that
people could hear the latest news
regarding threatened districts.
10 Paolo was half asleep because he
was 'yawning his head off'.
11 This disaster took place in the
mountains.

12a reports **b** thriving **c** reluctant
d wireless **e** proprietor **f** volunteer
g crammed **h** evacuees
13a The Red Cross was begun in 1864
by the Geneva Convention to provide
medical care for war casualties and
later to help victims of disasters, e.g.
earthquakes.
b Pestalozzi Children's Villages were
schools set up to care for refugee
children after WW2. Pestalozzi was a
Swiss educational reformer.
c Dewlaps are the loose bit of skin
hanging from the neck of a dog or
cattle.

Page 40 Adjectives (2)
A 1 thirsty **2** sleepy **3** stormy
4 showery
B 1 icy **2** shady **3** hazy **4** prickly
C 1 funny **2** muddy **3** furry **4** tinny
D 1 mischievous **2** skilful **3** expensive
4 dangerous
E 1 hasty **2** leaky **3** skinny **4** woolly
5 angry **6** poisonous **7** circular
8 juicy **9** accidental **10** dead
11 natural **12** expensive **13** sunny
14 sympathetic **15** deep

Page 41A One word for several
1 neighbours **2** bedroom **3** silently
4 queue **5** uncle **6** decided
7 autobiography **8** quarterly
9 famine **10** expand

B Incorrect sentences
1 Jamie played football with Peter and
me.
2 Mr. Peacock is the headmaster of a
girls' school.
3 The cat was run over by a car.
4 I'll share the sweets among Heather,
Paul and Elizabeth.
5 Look at the baby drinking from its
bottle.
6 Sam is nearly a year older than I.

7 Alan, Bob and Bill were sheltering
from the storm.
8 I have earned fewer house marks this
term.
9 "I didn't do anything wrong," sobbed
Mark.
10 Our teacher said he would teach me
to dive into the pool.
11 Frank is the taller of the two boys.
12 None of the pencils is sharp.

Page 42A Forming nouns from verbs
1 announced **2** decided **3** admired
4 discovered **5** relieved **6** fed
7 discover **8** invite **9** grow **10** know

B Forming nouns from verbs
1 arrival **2** behaviour **3** entrance
4 injury **5** performance **6** delivery
7 explosion **8** obedience **9** invention
10 decision

Page 43 Mixed bag (5)
A Odd one out
1 listen **2** modern **3** school **4** early
5 hole **6** square **7** cautious **8** tutor
9 deadly **10** scatter **11** loosen **12** loiter

B Opposites
The following are possible answers.
Accept anything that is opposite in
meaning to those given.
1 brave **2** irregular **3** miniscule
4 considerate **5** rough **6** normal
7 vertical **8** careful **9** rare

C Rhyming words
1 weight **2** rein **3** stretch **4** howl
5 court **6** beat **7** healed **8** tent

Page 44 Vocabulary and spelling
A 1 niece **2** handkerchief **3** ceiling
4 thief **5** believe **6** receive **7** piece
8 friend **9** deceive **10** height
B 1 dynamo **2** typewriter **3** hyacinth
4 hyena **5** dynamite **6** python
C 1 equator **2** escalator **3** author
4 spectator **5** corridor **6** projector

Page 45 Direct and indirect speech

A 1 Brian said he was tired after the long walk.

2 The caretaker said he'd lost his big brush.

3 The teacher said she'd/he'd lost her/his keys.

4 The teacher asked if anyone had found a bunch of keys.

5 Eric suggested that you could stay a little longer.

6 My dad advised me to try harder otherwise I'd never finish the job.

7 The old lady asked if you'd seen a black and white kitten.

8 Bill's friend warned him he mustn't play near the river.

9 He said he used to play for the first team.

10 Mr. Thomas said he was sure that you hadn't listened.

B 1 The boys said, "We're sorry for being late."

2 Mum said, "Dinner is ready."

3 The pilot remarked, "It may be a bumpy flight."

4 Tom said, "I will not be able to play."

5 Dora asked, "Are you going to town?"

6 The secretary said, "The paper is mine."

7 The teacher said, "I won't be away long."

8 The farmer explained, "I'm going to dig some drains."

9 The boy asked, "Mr. Aitken will you return my football?"

10 I asked Mr. Perkins, "Where are you going in August?"

Page 46 Comprehension (2)

1 The different kinds of bats found by the writer are the Horseshoe, the Natterer's, the Whiskered, the Long-eared and the Barbastelle.

2 The most common bat was the Horseshoe.

3 The White-waistcoat and Whiskered Bats were the most difficult to capture because they wedged themselves deep in the crevices of the cave.

4 Bats feed on insects.

5 The Horseshoe Bats are deep sleepers.

6 The Barbastelle bat makes a 'metallic buzz' sound.

7 The Natterer bat has a white underside whereas the Whiskered bat is a dusky colour.

8 A chrysalid is a butterfly or moth at a stage between larva and adult, when it is surrounded by a cocoon. The cocoon is like the sleeping bat's wings.

9 The rarest bat found in the caves is the Barbastelle.

10a profoundly **b** species **c** still **d** noticeable **e** inhabits **f** dubbed **g** crying **h** afford **i** abundant **j** transparent

Page 48 Mixed bag (6)

A 1 lion **2** monkey **3** giraffe **4** zebra **5** camel **6** kangaroo

B 1 pea **2** potato **3** onion **4** carrot **5** turnip **6** cabbage

C 1 ash **2** oak **3** pine **4** beech **5** cedar **6** chestnut

D 1 incorrect **2** impossible **3** irregular **4** disobedient **5** unwrap **6** inconvenient **7** uncomfortable **8** impolite **9** unfortunate **10** inexperienced **11** discomfort **12** irresponsible

E 1 taller **2** fastest **3** youngest **4** strongest **5** warmer **6** fattest **7** larger **8** better